Do Ants

And Other Poems for Children

Rachel Yorke

Do Ants Wear Pants and Other Poems for Children
by Rachel Yorke

Copyright 2013 Rachel Yorke

ISBN: 978-1-938886-82-9

I would like to thank my life coach, Denise Jacques at Azimuth Life Coaching, for helping to kick-start my writing career. It has had a huge and positive impact on my life and helped to improve my lifestyle dramatically. She assisted me by giving me the opportunities to stretch myself and reach valuable life goals. She has shown me that I CAN achieve anything I want to if I really want it enough.

http://azimuthlifecoaching.co.uk

Table of Contents

I Wrote on Some Paper

I wrote on some paper,
I scribbled in me book,
I jotted down some poems,
So come on! take a look.

Do Ants Wear Pants?

Do ants wear pants?
I really cannot say.
I've never given it a thought,
Ya never know they may.

Imagine the pant factory,
Where all the ants must go.
The material being measured,
For the worker ants to sew.

I wonder if they're stripy,
Yellow, blue or green.
I really do not know,
I've never really seen.

Imagine how they'd wash them.
Would they change them every day?
Would they use machines?
Or have a special set ant way.

I wonder if *they* worry,
If they're fat or thin.
Or would they make em stretchy,
To fit tightly to their skin.

I don't know what it is you think.
I really do not care.
It was just a thought I had,
Do ants have pants to wear?

I Wanna Write a Poem

I wanna write a poem!
But don't know where to start,
You've gotta be really clever,
Cos it's such a creative art.

I'm not good at choosing words,
And putting them together,
To create a masterpiece,
That will last forever and ever.

Oh silly me, look what I've done.
I've rhymed some words together.
And written myself a piece of art,
I know I'll keep forever!

My Brother is Disgusting

My brother is disgusting.
He really takes the mick.
If I told you what he does,
You'd soon be feeling sick.

Don't say I didn't warn you.
If you choose to carry on,
Being that you're still reading,
I'll tell you about our John.

He puts his bogies in a bag
And sells them for a pound.
He says they're rubber bullets,
That goes off without a sound.

Ear wax is his favourite,
He collects it in a jar,
He admires the different colours,
It's really quite bizarre.

The cheese he finds between his toes,
He collects in an old shoe.
I promise I'm not lying,
Honest it's all true!

So if you stay at our house,
Be warned he'll have yours to.
Ya bogies and your ear wax
And ya toe cheese in his shoe.

I Hate Being Sick!

I hate it when you're being sick
And it dribbles down your nose.
Especially when the chunky bits,
Spill onto your bed clothes.

The worst is when you do your best,
To catch it in your hands.
Cos all that seems to happen,
Is it spreads before it lands.

The thing that I don't really get
And really cannot bear.
Is when I'm leaning forward
And it gets all in my hair.

There's nothing worse than being sick.
Oh wait I tell a lie.
It's when you need a poo as well
And you ask the question why?

So when you're feeling really sick,
Use a bowl and not the loo.
Then if you get a sudden urge,
You can be sick *and* have a poo.

The Lolly in the Freezer

My lolly's in the freezer,
I can have it after tea.
Ummmm my favourite flavour,
Chocolate and raspberry.

But first I have to tackle,
The food in front of me.
Errrrr the yuckiest grub ever,
Is a plate of veg you see.

I can visualise my lolly,
All yummy soft and nice.
My mouth begins to water,
I can almost taste the raspberry ice.

Squinting with one eye,
I sit back in my chair,
I sigh with disappointment,
Eating veg is so not fair!

I can almost taste the yummy lolly,
My mouth begins to drool.
The smell of frozen chocolate
And raspberry are so cool.

Now I look down at my plate
And place my head into my hands,
The disappointment stays upon my face,
Cos the veggie rule still stands

Can't wait to hold my lolly
And see it on its stick.
Breathe in the cold aroma,
Before going in for my first lick.

So holding my nose tightly,
I eat the veggies quick.
The more I shovel down my throat,
The more I feel sick.

Racing to the freezer,
I was feeling kind of jolly,
Searching through the ice-creams,
To find my favourite lolly.

Tearing off the wrapper,
I've waited for so long.
I really don't feel hungry,
Is that so very wrong?

My Very Clever Friend

My friend is very clever,
She's never ever wrong,
She always knows just what to say,
That's why we get along.

She's always full of good advice
And helps to make things right.
Even when I'm feeling cross,
She's always so polite.

She ignores me when I'm silly
And smiles when I'm a fool,
I reckon she's so clever,
Impressive and so cool!

She uses such big words to talk,
I don't know what she means.
But after explanation,
It usually helps me with my dreams.

To me she's very special,
An angel in disguise,
Full of intuition,
Intelligent and wise.

What a clever friend I have,
All positive and polite.
And if you've never met her yet,
Be warned she's very bright!

Our Pet Bob

Bob is our pet,
He comes and he goes,
Where he goes to,
Nobody knows.

His visits are short.
He doesn't stay long.
We love Bob to visit
But our friends say it's wrong.

When we all see Bob,
We all say hi.
When others see Bob,
They want him to die.

He changes in size,
Every time he appears.
One of our friends,
He reduces to tears!

Bob is OUR pet,
We ask him to stay
But when he decides,
He just crawls away.

Poor old Bob,
He's misunderstood.
Why can't others,
See spiders are good!

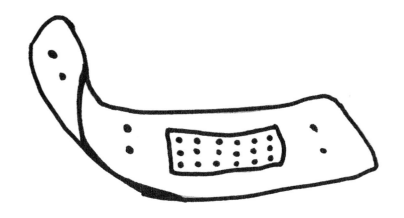

Plaster Disaster

Oh my goodness, it's not good.
It's really quite a disaster.
The blood it's pouring everywhere,
Oh quick I need a plaster!

The blood it's getting everywhere,
I think I'm gonna die,
I really don't know what to do,
I just know I'm *not* to cry.

Oh phew! My life is saved at last,
My friend has fetched her Mum.
And through my gritted teeth I cry,
"I'm really glad you've come."

Clare's Mum said "how ya doing?"
Then caught the sight of blood.
She took a mighty gasp of air,
Before dropping with a thud.

The ambulance arrived in five,
And took away Clare's Mum,
But not before the plaster,
Was put on my sore thumb.

Half Term

Half term is here,
It's time for fun.
No school all week,
Oh come on sun!

A Batch a Balm Cake or Bread Roll

A batch, a balm cake, or bread roll.
A cob, a bun, or bap.
So many names to call one thing,
Dictated by the map.

Do you wear a house coat,
a robe or dressing gown?
So many names to call one thing,
Depending on your town.

A jitty, alley, entry.
A ginnel, or a gulley.
So many names to call one thing,
It's hard to grasp it fully.

It's funny how the language used,
Is very much the same.
Showing where you come from,
By the item's given name.

But no matter where you come from,
No matter where you live.
We all understand each other,
And laugh at the names we give.

My Hated Haircut

I had my hair cut yesterday;
I hate it with a passion.
Mum always uses a bowl n comb,
and it's totally out of fashion.

The hair it fell down past my face,
and I just wanted to cry.
Mum just kept on cutting,
as I gave a great big sigh.

When the cut was over
and I looked into the mirror.
The look that came upon my face
just couldn't be any clearer.

My Mum says "oh how lovely",
but I had to bite my tongue.
Because it was so ugly
and it was so very wrong.

My Brother Really Stinks!

My brother Maxwell really stinks!
No matter where we are.
The worst is when we're traveling,
And we're trapped inside the car.

Ya know when he has done it,
Cos he gives a cheeky smile
And before you get to realise,
It's up your nose and vile.

It really doesn't smell nice
And you have to hold your nose.
There's nowhere to escape from it,
Too late! It's on your clothes.

It's like a deathly poison,
It's powerful and so hostile.
It really lingers in the air,
And hangs around a while.

We wind down all the windows,
It really doesn't help.
We look like we've gone really mad,
As the wind carries along our yelps.

Eventually the smell it goes,
And we've gone another mile.
Oh no! Here we go again,
As Maxwell smiles a cheeky smile.

The Squirrel in the Garden

Looking out the window,
Staring back at me,
Was a curious animal,
It made me jump you see.

Wonder what he's thinking,
Don't know what he'd do,
Does he have a family?
Will they visit too?

Standing tall and slender,
Will he move or not?
Will he make a run for it?
Or stay frozen to the spot.

He doesn't move a muscle,
His tail pulled in tight,
I only moved a little,
And he ran away in fright.

He jumped upon the table,
Then climbed upon the fence,
By the time he reached the roof top,
He was looking rather tense.

His eyes as big as saucers,
He spots himself a meal,
He scampers on the bird house,
And began to make a steal,

Wonder where he comes from?
Wonder where he lives?
A very cheeky fellow,
With a great initiative.

Filled with all the nuts and seeds
It's time for him to go
He springs around the garden
Putting on quite a show

He stands upon the dustbin
And turns to look at me
Then bounds into the distance
And vanishes up a tree

Wonder where he's gone to?
Wonder if he's ok?
I thank him for his visit,
'cos it brightened up my day.

Animals Are Funny

An elephant dancing in his pants,
Is a funny sight to see
But what really makes me giggle and laugh
Is a monkey drinking tea.

A mouse in his Pyjamas,
And a zebra wearing jeans,
A parrot with a coat on,
It's crazy by all means.

Animals are really funny,
When you stop and look.
I love escaping to my world,
When I read my favourite book.

My Music Is My World

My music can be powerful,
Whether happy or subdued,
It can change the way I view things,
It can change my every mood.

When I put my iPod on
And carefully choose my song.
Listening soulfully to the words,
I can't help but sing along.

Music can bring me laughter,
Or even make me cry.
Depending on the track I choose,
Can dictate a smile or sigh.

The longer that I listen,
I simply disappear.
It takes me to another place,
Where lyrics are crystal clear.

The music flows around my head,
The rhythm and the beat.
It travels through my body,
From my head down to my feet.

A world away from everything,
I simply can't explain.
A magic it takes over,
Where only happy thoughts remain.

Now the song has ended
And real life is back,
Do I go on living?
Or choose another track?

My Mum's Knitting

Mum went to get her knitting
And this is what she found.
A very holey jumper
And wool that's all unwound.

Looking really puzzled,
She simply couldn't speak.
She only started knitting,
The beginning of last week.

Shrieking and wailing,
She jumped up on a chair.
Before shouting really loudly,
There's a mouse over there!

I hurried quickly to the bag,
Carrying a shoe.
But all I found inside the bag,
Was a load of old mouse pooh.

Looking closely at the wool,
With some grumbles and some groans.
I realised what it was I saw,
It was a set of old mouse bones.

I began to realise quickly,
She started knitting this for me.
Last week seemed such a time ago,
Cos now I'm 33!

My Dog And Cat Are All Mixed Up

My dog and cat are all mixed up,
We're really not amused.
Amazingly they get it wrong,
They're simply all confused.

The cat he thinks he is a dog,
The dog he thinks a cat.
They really need to sort it out,
And have themselves a chat.

The dog he brings us mice and birds,
The cat just wants some fuss.
They've really got to change their ways,
If they want to stay with us.

The cat chases the postman,
The dog just sleeps a lot.
They really need to get a grip,
They've simply lost the plot.

But even though they're back to front,
We must be part to blame.
It really isn't all their fault,
We love them all the same.

One Day I Went Off to the Coast

One day I went off to the coast,
a day trip to remember.
I always choose the month of June
because it's cold in December.

I Love it when the sea is calm
It brings to me a smile.
I sit and watch the clouds pass by,
Then walk another mile.

As the time just passes by
And daytime turns to night,
I turn to see my shadow,
Under the beauty of moonlight.

Now the trip has ended,
It's time for me to go
But memories last forever,
and I can visit again I know.

A Family Party to Remember

Family Parties bring a smile,
They're always so much fun.
Especially garden parties,
Where we can play out in the sun.

One Party always comes to mind,
It's one I remember most.
Was supposed to be a BBQ,
But all we ate was toast.

Cos over in the corner,
Beyond the massive queue.
Was where my uncle master chef,
Had burnt the BBQ.

There were cousins running everywhere,
Aged 2 - 34.
Some I've never, ever met
And some well, say no more.

Mum was really funny,
Playing host to all the guests.
Asking 20 questions each,
Without stopping for a rest.

Dad was playing football,
He thought he was a star.
Until it hit the tree branch,
And broke the window on his car!

My brother was on the bouncy castle,
He was bouncing really high
And when the castle went off bang,
You should have seen him fly!

My sister is the funniest,
She tripped and broke her shoe.
She dived and gambolled past me,
Knocking over Dad's home brew.

It was a party to remember,
All services were there.
The ambulance, fire and police,
ate toast it's only fair!

When the party ended,
and everyone had gone.
Mum and Dad they must be mad,
Cos they've planned another one.

Printed in Great Britain
by Amazon

11165688R00031